LIGHT

Written by trish MICHAEL
Illustrated by Julia Liadovski

May you set free your burdens
and be the light you were put here to be.

The world is full of choices.
Your mind is full of thoughts.
Some are like balloons,
Others cinder blocks.

Some thoughts are uplifting.
They guide you to the sky.
They make your life feel better.
And toward your best you'll fly.

Others make you feel bad
And soon enough you'll know,
You've got yourself a cinder block
Weighing down your flow.

At first you may not notice.
It may seem all right.
But as you travel forward,
Balloons move out of sight.

For once you have a cinder block
You'll sink hard to the ground.
Attracting other cinder blocks.
The heaviness compounds.

You may still see balloons
And reach with all your might.
But cinder blocks are heavy.
The reach becomes a fight.

As you gather cinder blocks,
The people that you'll find,
Will have their own collections
Weighing down their minds.

It might feel quite normal.
You may not even whine.
And you might start to tell yourself
"These cinder blocks are fine."

But there will be things out there
You'll want to see or do.
They may feel impossible
With so much weight on you.

And there may be new people
You want to have around.
But those that hold balloons
Don't stay long on the ground.

Even if they wanted,
They never could have stayed.
Because for them to do so,
They'd have to make a trade.

Their lightness for your heavy.
Balloons must be let go,
And as they sink down to you,
Away their dreams will go.

That's no way to treat others,
To act just like a leech–
Expect them to forget balloons
Because you cannot reach.

Instead there's a solution.
Although it may be hard,
Each moment holds the answer,
And you can play the card.

Balloons are always out there.
You simply need to choose.

Would I like to win?
Or would I like to lose?

Once you make the statement,
"It's time for me to win!",
Once you've dropped some cinder blocks,
Think good thoughts again.

You'll notice you feel lighter.
You'll find you feel more *you*.
You'll see that new balloons
Are floating right to you!

You'll maybe even grab some,
And lift up off the ground.
But your light just can't happen,
If you're still tethered down.

As you move towards freedom,
You'll have to have some talks.
With all those heavy people,
And all their cinder blocks.

If they can't let theirs go,
You can't keep them around.
If they don't want balloons,
They'll simply weigh you down.

And though that may cause sadness,
You can be the light.
For when they see you floating,
They may start their own flight;

Toward making better choices,
And finding their own way.
Maybe you'll even meet them,
Up in the sky one day.

That is what I'm hoping,
As I move apart,
From those who choose the cinder blocks,
Though they have my heart.

I'm floating with balloons.
I'll keep sending you some.
I'm headed toward the happy.
I'd love it if you'd come.